'...then: the main purpose of my life was to be a patient

now: I am a person...'

Jack Royall

best wishes

Jack Royall

Oct 2024

First Edition
First Printed in 2024

ISBN 978 1 3999 8533 8

J WJ RoyallPublishing
Norwich

jackroyall92@gmail.com

Printed by Gowise Print, 4 Belmore Road,
Thorpe St Andrew, Norwich NR7 0PT
www.gowise.co.uk
Tel: (01603) 431304

Woodland
CARBON
www.woodlandcarbon.co.uk
GOWISE PRINT
Printed on Carbon Captured paper

Gowise Print is a member of the Carbon Capture Scheme in partnership with the Woodland Trust. With regular donations to the Trust on paper purchases and also direct contribution, the print company aims to fully offset the CO2 emissions from print production and also production of this paper. The Trust actively plants trees in the UK and protects trees and ancient woodland.

Introduction to Jack's Story

It's a pleasure to write this introduction for Jack's story having known him and followed his progress for over twenty years.

Jack is one of those people dealt a very difficult hand when he was born but together with those who love him, he has dealt with every new problem and managed to thrive where anyone with less courage and determination would have crumbled

As you will read, he has encountered one life changing problem after another but somehow he and his family have summoned up the resources to find the best path through and remain optimistic no matter how many battles they have had.

Severe illness in early childhood often leaves lifelong scars. But Jack has had no time to dwell on his difficulties as after overcoming each another equally bad or worse new one was always round the corner. But like an Olympic canoeist shooting ever more tricky rapids Jack has travelled on, Always hopeful, usually smiling and never really looking back.

It was very fortunate that when Jack faced his toughest challenge medical science had progressed enough to find him a magic bullet. But even that was not easy for him to access. He and his family had to fight for treatment for himself, and later he helped lead the fight to make the treatment available for others.

As a doctor my job is to support patients through the most difficult times in their life. With Jack it is sometimes difficult to know who is supporting who. It has always been a pleasure and a tonic to see him in clinic.

One day, when it is time for me to hang up my stethoscope, Jack's story is something I will remember with pleasure during my retirement.

Dr Chris Kingswood MBBS MSc FRCP

One *PILL* - One *LIFE*

From a baby with a life-threatening illness

to

A boy with life-saving surgery

to

A man with a life-changing pill

Explanations Surrounding the TSC World

TSC:
Tuberous Sclerosis Complex is a rare genetic disorder that affects the skin and nervous system. It may cause white skin patches, red or brown birthmarks and/or a facial rash across the cheeks and nose. Also, seizures, delayed mental development, and mainly non-cancerous tumours, particularly in the brain, retina, kidneys, heart and skin. Many patients have autism or display autistic or aspergers tendencies and behavioural issues.

There are two genes which cause TSC – TSC1 on chromosome 9 and TSC2 on chromosome 16. Both genes work together. There are lots of different mutations of TS and although genetic faults have been found in a huge percentage of blood samples in research situations, this figure varied slightly in clinical laboratories.

TSA:
Tuberous Sclerosis Association is a self-help organisation located in the UK and established in 1977 by a group of parents and interested physicians dedicated to providing support to those with TSC and their families by raising awareness and promoting fundraising activities for research projects.

SEGA:
Subependymal Giant Cell Astrocytoma.
A slow growing benign tumour that is almost exclusively associated with TSC and develops in 5% - 20% of patients.

OMMAYA RESERVOIR:
This is a small plastic device implanted into the brain so that medicines can be delivered directly. Also, it enables doctors to take samples of fluid from the spinal cord.

THE DRUG:
The medication first introduced as RAD011 (later named Everolimus) as a potential treatment for patients with certain symptoms of TSC

THE TRIAL:
A five year double-blind trial of the drug first introduced in the UK in 2010 by the Drug Company - Novartis Pharmaceuticals

One *PILL* - One *LIFE*

There are many people and organisations that I have thanked whilst writing this account of my life; people who have contributed (and still do) to my care and welfare, others are mentioned below and in the final chapter.

However, I can't open my story without saying one great big THANKS to my Mum Alison (Ali) for her dedication to keeping me alive and for doing the very best for me especially in the early days when TSC was hardly recognised, and for what she still does for me on a daily basis.

From the research which she carried out, with very little information to go on 30 years ago, but with a lot of determination, she was able to understand what was going on with me. Through this understanding she was able to help the various health, education and social professionals, that we met along the way, to be aware of TSC and its implications.

To my beloved sister and dearest friend India (Indie) for all the scary years, especially when we were young, Sorry Indie!

And then there's thanks to my Nanny Pam (that's Mum's Mum) who has spent a long, long time talking to me and wading through my Journal with me so that we could extract and collate relevant information to enable us to put together this legible summary of what I hope has resulted in an interesting account of my life!

One *PILL* - One *LIFE*

One *PILL* - One *LIFE*

1

The Early Days

My name is Jack Royall and I'm now 32 years old. Life is ok for me now but it hasn't always been that way, you see I have the genetic condition – Tuberous Sclerosis Complex. For those who're not familiar with this illness, I'll tell you how its affected my life, and that of my family...

This part of my story tells of the problems that faced me and my family before I was able to have any recollection of what went on, so I've written it with the help of family members, and friends, with their memories of the anxieties and the worrying times leading up to, and after, my diagnosis.

In February 1992, when Mum was seven months pregnant with me, she became poorly and developed a little known condition known as symphysis pubis dysfuction (now called pelvic girdle pain). This resulted in Mum going into hospital for a while. When she came home she was in a wheelchair for the remainder of the pregnancy. She was induced at 38 weeks to relieve the pain.

After three days of a very difficult labour I was finally born on 6th April 1992 by ventouse delivery as there were complications and risks to me. I was a poorly newborn. Mum had to have blood transfusions. We spent a week in hospital until I was allowed to go home. So you'll see that things got off to a bad start! But Mum and Dad were so proud of me, a bonny little boy who seemed content whilst in their arms.

We went back to our one-bedroom, upstairs flat in Norwich, where my parents' lives changed completely. At the time we were unaware of my illness and what was to become a long journey ahead of us.

Despite the bad start I progressed nicely as a young baby; Mum breast fed me, but I would only take a few sucks and I just wanted to be comforted by Mum's loving warm heartbeat. I was the apple of Mum and

Dad's eye; a much wanted little baby boy named Jack William James Royall.

The name Jack is after my paternal Grandfather, who had died when Dad was only 18; and then William James, is a mixture of my Dad's name and my Mum's stepdad, who died three months before I was born. Therefore, and unfortunately, we never got to know each other.

I cut my teeth and sat up early, and was very alert and active. However, there was one thing I didn't like and that was food. Milk was too yummy! I had no desire to be weaned on to solids. Here came my parent's first battle with their *'angel'*. After trying all types of weaning methods, they took me to the doctors. I just wanted my milk and found the taste and texture of food too disgusting. No matter how hard they tried my mouth would seal shut like a zip with a 'No Entry Allowed' sign.

Dad would become frustrated and Mum anxious. My Nanny Pam (Mum's Mum) would try to encourage me with games like *'Choo-Choo'* train in the tunnel, but my mouth was not a tunnel, and it remained sealed. I would rip my hair out and bite myself in protest. I guess these were the first signs that all was not perfect as Mum and Dad had hoped.

2

Warning Signs

Our little flat was cramped; almost every day Mum pushed me in my pram to a deli not far away. Then on to a local department store to meet Nanny Pam for coffee in her lunch break.

Nanny was working fulltime in a nearby office and after she left us to go back to work we walked to the Early Learning store to play with the toys there. Then we went to another store where my Mum's Auntie Trish (Nanny Pam's sister) worked and she'd join us for coffee there. Later we walked to Chapelfield Gardens, close to where we lived. Mum pushed me on the swings and then we headed home. That just about summed up the daily routine (during the week) for Mum and me during the early days of my life.

When I was 13 months Mum and Dad took me to Orlando, America, to see my Uncle Glenn who was living in Florida. During that visit we went to Disneyworld where I became very ill. I was hospitalised and told that I was having febrile convulsions. On reflection, these were probably my first seizures. I didn't get to see very much of Orlando as I was too ill. Ever since I learned about this episode in my life I've always wanted to go back to see what I missed out on! I eventually fulfilled that dream, but more about that later in my story.

This is a picture of Dad holding me while at Disneyworld

When we returned home from America my personality began changing; I became more aggressive, to not just Mum and Dad, but also to myself and anyone else who came near me.

I was having constant ear infections, glue ear, they called it. I was always at the doctors for one thing or another so I was forever on antibiotics. Mum mentioned to the doctors about my difficult behaviour and lack of progress in normal eating habits. With regard to the latter, I had developed an obsession for eating paper, cardboard and string. Mum couldn't leave a newspaper around, and the toilet roll had to be put well out of my reach. Tissues were my favourite!!

The doctors referred me to be assessed and a specialist saw for herself the extremes of my behaviour. She was concerned about the aggression that I showed towards her and others in the room.

The assessments resulted in me being referred for further investigations by the paediatric dept at the Jenny Lind hospital in Norwich (the children's department of the Norfolk & Norwich University hospital) in an effort to discover what was causing my problems.

Two pictures of me as a toddler

When I was about 16 months Mum and Dad took me to the shop at Carrow Road, the home of Norwich City Football Club; they wanted to buy me some PJ's in Norwich City colours - yellow and green.

We were on the way home when a passer-by spoke to my parents and told them that their child in the back-pack-carrier seemed to be unconscious and was blue in the face. Dad quickly pulled me from his back and found that the man had probably saved my life as Mum and Dad were completely unaware of the distress I was in as I was out of their sight in the carrier.

The vigilant passer-by called for an ambulance. The crew gave me oxygen, resuscitated me and whisked us off to the local hospital where I was assessed and admitted to the Jenny Lind, a place that would become very familiar to me and my family over the following years!

I was in hospital for about four days on that first occasion and was put on more antibiotics as, yet again, I had another ear infection. Once again Mum and Dad were told it was a febrile convulsion, with no further investigations at that time.

After the short stay I had recovered enough to go home. Little did Mum and Dad know on that day that this was the beginning of a regular occurrence as it became a way of life for me and my parents.

Over a period of time it became apparent that any infections (ears, nose, throat and chest - and they occurred quite frequently) would trigger a another convulsion where resuscitation was often needed to bring me out. My condition hadn't been diagnosed at that time and Mum and Dad were really worried about me as they didn't know the reason for me being so poorly.

3

The Diagnosis

On one occasion when I was in hospital following a seizure, my Nanny Pam was at home listening to an early morning programme on local radio. She was getting ready to come to see me before going to work. She heard the radio presenter interviewing a local lady who was the mother of a boy with TSC. They were discussing the discovery of the first defective chromosome to be identified. They mentioned seven of the symptoms that TSC sufferers can display. Nanny had never heard of the condition but thought to herself, *Jack has at least five of those.*

At those times when I was in hospital, Nanny would come early in the morning and sit with me so that Mum and Dad (who had spent the night at my bedside hoping that I would pull through) could go off together and have a few quiet moments to themselves, to have breakfast, and to freshen up.

When she was by my bed and Mum and Dad had gone off for breakfast, she discussed what she'd heard on the radio with a member of the nursing staff. On my parents' return Nanny thought she ought to tell them what she had done so they would be prepared if anyone came to speak to them. No-one came back with comments on the subject, and as soon as I was well enough, we all went home.

The same thing happened a few weeks later when yet again I was admitted. Nanny spoke to a different staff member about her concern that I may have Tuberous Sclerosis, but on my recovery we were discharged without reference to it and no diagnosis.

Following the third time when, once again, Nanny had brought this to the attention of the medical staff, but nothing was said so, when I was well enough, we went home. That evening Mum got a 'phone call from the hospital saying they would like her to bring me back for some specific tests.

Scans and tests were used to make a diagnosis, together with a Woods Light (that's a special lamp that, when shone on the skin, will show any irregularities in the structure of the skin) the many tests etc revealed that I had skin lesions that weren't visible to the naked eye, and I had four tumours in my brain.

Other symptoms of my condition were behavioural and development disorders. At that time my heart, kidneys, eyes and liver were not affected by tumours (they came later). Although not diagnosed as autistic, I displayed autistic tendencies; all these are well recognised symptoms of TSC.

Following a review of my behaviour and the results of tests it was confirmed that I had Tuberous Sclerosis Complex! I was around two years old at the time of diagnosis.

Sleep patterns, and consequently, those of my parents, were highly disrupted. Confused and afraid Mum started to make enquiries and do some research. My parents and loved ones had to come to terms with the fact that I had an incurable genetic condition.

Mum and Dad made contact with the people at the Tuberous Sclerosis Association, who were such a help to us all. A quote of Mum's at the time went as follows:

'The TSA has been fantastic, they are there to help you through it day to day and also fund research. I don't know how we would manage without it.'

Genetic counselling was put in place to check if I had inherited the condition from either parent. They were told this was not so in my case, but that my TSC was a new mutation.

Mum was already in the early stages of another pregnancy. It was a very difficult time as she thought there was a chance that the new baby may also have the condition even though mine was a new mutation; not proven to be hereditary. Mum and Dad wanted another baby but not right at that time!

As I was such a handful they had decided to delay starting another baby until a bit later when they hoped my condition may be more manageable. But, a little one was on the way, and Mum had a belief… she had faith that the baby had been sent to them before my diagnosis so that they would be spared the heart-rending decision as to when, or if, they would have more children in the light of my diagnosis.

And so, a new baby was on the way, and the pregnancy continued!

Whilst Mum was pregnant she had to have a special scan called a foetal echocardiogram on the baby's heart in an effort to identify if there were any cardiac rhabdomyomas (non-cancerous tumours), If they were present, this could indicate TSC in the unborn baby.

Below you can see a photo of me on a TSA flyer advertising a TS awareness event: I was four at the time.

October 1996;
Coffee and Christmas Cards
"Working together we can make a difference"

4

India Arrives

My little sister was born in the NNUH at 4pm on 29th September 1994. Mum was delivering India with Dad at her side whilst Nanny Pam was at my bedside on the floor below (intensive care) watching over me as I recovered from yet another seizure which required resuscitation.

And so it went on, one fit after another; one hospital visit after another; no proper eating pattern; aggressive behaviour, many unusual obsessions and hyper-activity; I was always running; it seemed that I couldn't walk anywhere… I just ran; this created a challenge for both my parents, when all the time they were trying to care for my little sister, India, as well.

In addition to these symptoms, I was obsessive about logos; everywhere I went I would see and recognise advertising logos. If I stood at the top of a very busy road and asked to explain what I could see, I wouldn't mention buses, shops or people, I would see only the tiniest logo on the tee-shirt of a passerby, or a sweet-paper drifting in the breeze.

15

When taken for a ride in the car I wouldn't see other vehicles but I would see the smallest familiar or new symbol hidden within the sign-writing on a van or lorry. I would see a logo on a decaying chocolate wrapper which, long ago, had been thrown from the window of a passing car and was now hiding in the long grass of the verge.

I was particularly attracted to the Tuberous Sclerosis Association logo whenever I saw it on paperwork that Mum had around the house.

Picture of the TSA Logo

When India was still just a baby we moved from our small upstairs flat into a three bedroom council house on the Heartsease Housing Estate which is on the outskirts of Norwich. This made my parents' lives easier as there was much more space, and now a garden for India and me to play in.

Some of the people we met whilst living there have become good lifetime friends (*we call them our Heartsease Friends*). They have given valuable help to our family over many years. Without their neighbourly support life would have been far more difficult, especially for Mum.

When I was about three Mum was in need of a break so it was arranged that I would start nursery school for a few hours each day so that she could have a little special time with India, who was at risk of being overlooked because of my many and complicated needs. I seemed to get on well there and enjoyed the stimulation of staff and other children.

One aspect of my personality proved to be a bit difficult for the staff in that I was obsessive about washing my hands! I felt compelled to do it on and off all day long, especially if I had been in the sandpit; textures such as this made my hands feel unbearable. My eating habits, although better, were still difficult and challenging!

The severity and symptoms of Tuberous Sclerosis Complex varies from one person to another. Some people go undiagnosed for a lifetime. Others are diagnosed with a mild case and live full and independent lives. But those severely affected suffer a range of disabilities. It is thought that one in 6000 people have TSC   Its estimated that only one third of children born with the disease have inherited the condition, otherwise it will be a spontaneous genetic mutation. In the case of spontaneous mutation, the cause is still unknown!

A newborn baby stands a 50:50 chance of inheriting TSC if one parent has the condition. If that parent is very mildly affected, he/she may remain undiagnosed until a child of theirs has been found to have TSC. The severity of the condition in a child born to a parent with TSC can vary considerably.

Two faulty genes have been identified (TSC1 or TSC2). Only one of these needs to be defective to cause the condition. Although tumours are not always cancerous they can grow within themselves and this can adversely affect the patient.

Although autism/aspergers syndrome is very frequently associated with TSC, it doesn't necessarily follow that being born with TSC will result in you being on the spectrum. Who knows, I may have had aspergers even if I didn't have TSC!

5

Fundraising and Other Events

During 1995, when I was still three years old, with the help of the Tuberous Sclerosis Association, Mum and Dad launched an appeal to raise awareness and funds for the TSA to support families and research programmes.

One of the activities was that my Dad, who had a long blonde pony tail that had taken ten years to grow, had his head shaven to raise funds. Another event was a charity disco which was held at a nearby venue in Norwich. Local well-known DJs and companies supported the cause on the night.

A parachute jump, a few abseils and a zip-fly across the River Clyde were other challenges taken on by Dad, all organised with the help of the TSA. Later, there was a charity football match. Mum and Dad were able to hand a nice fat cheque to the TSA later that year.

In July 1995 former Olympic Skating Champions (who were patrons of the TSA at the time) were performing in Norwich. It was arranged that they would meet me, with

Mum and Nanny Pam. This gave national publicity for the appeal. Although I was just three years old I vaguely remember meeting them on a sunny July afternoon and presenting them with a small bouquet of flowers as a *Thank You* for sparing time out from their tight schedule to meet us and support our campaign.

Again in1995, and then later in 1997, because of my unusual illness, I was invited to take part in the Royal College of Physicians' Examinations for trainee doctors, hosted by the NNUH's Jenny Lind Department. The hospital invited patients with certain conditions to come along and have face to face consultations and examinations in the diagnosis part of the trainee doctors' exams. As a result, I was awarded Certificates of Merit by the Royal College of Physicians – a copy of the Certificate is on the next page:

Photo of my family fundraising for the TSA

**ROYAL COLLEGE OF PAEDIATRICS
AND CHILD HEALTH**

CERTIFICATE OF MERIT

Has been awarded to

..................Jack Royall..........................

For helping Medical and Nursing Staff on

..........Friday 26 October 2007..................

Consultant Paediatrician.................................

Sister ....

Photo of certificate of Merit Issued by the
Royal College of Paediatrics and
Child Health

22

When Mum was a girl she kept a diary, and when she went on trips, holidays or outings, she made a scrap book, or her Journal, as she called it. Thankfully, Mum always encouraged and helped me to do the same, so I have pictures and accounts of many of the events during my life. Without my Journal it would be difficult, if not impossible, for me to recall all the things I can now include in this story.

Apart from the presentation of the Certificates of Merit and the flowers to the ice skaters, I have little or no recollection of events described in the previous chapters.

Now I will tell you of the events affecting my life as I have seen them for myself or as I can recapture them with the help of my Journal.

6

Starting School

I started mainstream school in September 1997. This was just down the road from where we lived. Although I had difficulty with concentration and my fine motor skills were poor I managed to keep up with the rest of the class. I learned quickly and my reading abilities were well above average.

Starting school at Heartsease Infants

Douglas House is a remote facility of the Cambridge University and Addenbrooke's Hospital. It's a Department of Psychiatry; the centre specialises in the study of intellectual and developmental disabilities in children and adolescents. Also, its a centre of excellence for those with autism/aspergers syndrome.

At the age of five I was referred there and I was tested by a professional psychologist and when the results came through it was shown that my IQ and reading levels were equal to a 15 year old. However, I found writing very difficult, but on a mental test I was the only kid in my class to get 10 out of 10 for spellings on a continuous basis.

My progress was going in the right direction even though I had been statemented and I was often off school due to health problems.

One thing really bugged me, because of my seizures I wasn't allowed to take part in sporting activities, because when I was younger I had problems with my hypothalamus (one of its roles is to govern body temperature). Any over-heating as a result of physical activities, or infections, would trigger a seizure and off I'd go again to hospital to be resuscitated!

The local ambulance crews got to know me well, and Mum had to be taught how to do the resuscitation in case the ambulance was delayed. I realise now what a stress this must have been for Mum and Dad.

My eating habits had changed, but not much over the years, I still couldn't eat much in the way of a varied diet, but I did like grapes, raisins, poppy-seeds and flaked almonds. I had an absolute obsession about these foods and survived on little else, except food capsules that had been prescribed for me.

Different foods on my plate were not allowed to touch each other, and I would clear up one thing before moving on to the next. Although I'm much better now and I will eat almost anything, its still the case that I feel compelled to eat one part of the meal before starting on another!

When I was small I had several obsession regarding food and eating habits! One was that I liked to sip water or milk from a saucer like a kitten or puppy. That was then, but not now! Thankfully, I've outgrown that obsession!

One of my favourite pastimes was drawing cartoons. I was inclined to have obsessions about certain things, including cards and various merchandise relating to certain cartoon characters.

7

Sleep-overs

Dad was in the building trade and the economy had gone into a recession. There was little or no work around for him. He made a decision to retrain and went to an academy just outside Norwich to learn the skills of an off-shore worker in the oil industry. He soon passed all the tests and found work on the oil rigs in the North Sea, just off Great Yarmouth, and later much further afield.

He was often away for weeks at a time while Mum was at home with me and India trying desperately to cope with a worsening situation.

She had the support of Nanny Pam but even she couldn't be there all the time. She had been widowed three months before I was born and she had to work hard to look after herself. The Heartsease Friends were there and helped, but they had jobs and families of their own.

Every Friday evening when Nanny Pam got home from work India and I would go to hers for a sleepover. Neither of us slept very well and Nanny would put nice smelly oils about the place and read stories and play soothing music. I remember that cassette so well, it was called Crystal Healing. And she had a lamp that when switched on reflected various shapes around the ceiling of the room – those moving shapes and the music mesmerised me and helped lull me into sleep.

Even at that young age I loved music and the sound of that gentle rhythm would soon quieten me down and persuade me to stay in my bed until I drifted off. I'm not sure if it had the same affect on India who was just as hyper-active as me, if not more so, although she doesn't have TSC.

At some time in the night, I expect Nanny must have turned off the music and the light because they weren't there when I woke up. This piece of music and the light were kept exclusively to induce sleep and weren't used at any other time.

Nanny took us home on Saturday afternoons. When Dad was away Nanny and Mum would spend the rest of the day together chatting about things and playing with us. Often they would take us out for a ride in the car or go to the seaside to let off steam on the beach.

I really wasn't very keen on the beach; as soon as my bare toes touched the sand I wanted to go home, and I would go into a tantrum, much to the annoyance of India who wanted to play there all day. I wasn't even happy to go there in my socks and shoes.

There was something about the grains of sand that I couldn't cope with. Even now I don't really like it too much, but I will do it to please others, something I wouldn't do when in my younger, more selfish, days. At that time I had no wish to do anything I didn't like just to please my sister, or anyone else come to that! Even now, I never take off my shoes and socks on the beach!!

Even with help, Mum was collapsing under the strain of trying to cope on her own with Dad working so far away off-shore.

Nanny Pam and me aged about 3

8

A Turning Point

One Saturday after Nanny Pam had taken us home after
our sleep-over, she had to leave to go visit a sick friend.
After Nanny left Mum took me and India out to a place
where kids can eat and then go into the play area. During
the afternoon I had a really bad seizure and India was
frightened and distressed by the fuss that it caused in the
venue. Mum was asked by the management to take us
away and not come back as we were disturbing others
visitors!

That was the last straw, Mum tells me that she cannot
remember anything after putting us both in the car and
driving home, until the next day when, late afternoon,
Nanny turned up and found the house in an absolute
mess.

My own memory of all this is not entirely clear, and
what I can recall is quite painful. I do remember that at
some time during Sunday morning one of our Heartsease
Friend's sons noticed that our curtains weren't opened
and that India was sitting on the window-sill crying, she
was just three at the time. The boy's Mum came to the

house and found the door unlocked and two small children in a state of distress. She found Mum fast asleep upstairs and left her there, but left a note in the kitchen to say that she had taken us home with her to clean us up and to feed us.

Just before tea-time that Sunday Nanny came to the house and found Mum just waking up, she was unable to say what had happened after management had chucked us out of the venue the previous day.

The full details of this episode are best left unrecorded, but it's enough to say that Nanny sent for Dad to come home immediately from his oil-rig job. At the time he was based off the shores of Jamaica. He arrived home on the Tuesday.

To cut a long story short, Mum had had a breakdown and was admitted to a special hospital where she stayed for several weeks. Nanny got compassionate leave from work to look after us. Occasionally we were allowed to visit Mum in hospital and gradually she improved enough to come home. A social worker was appointed to take care of the well-being of me and India.

We struggled on with hospital appointments and unscheduled visits as epileptic attacks grabbed me again and yet again. India's life was being turned upside down as well.

To try to help me and India over a rough time Dad and Mum got us a puppy; a Jack Russell, which we named Saxon. India loved the little thing but I really didn't take to it. I'm sure it did her some good. But I found that all Saxon would do is bark and growl at me; I think he was being aggressive towards me because he knew I didn't like him.

At this point in my life I started to have a few unusual experiences. It may have been as a result of one of the various medicines I was on, but we'll never really know. For example, on one occasion when me and my family were in a restaurant in Norwich I had a vision of my paternal grandfather. I could actually visualise what he looked like and what he was wearing. I hadn't seen any photos of my granddad but Dad later confirmed that the way I had described him, even down to the clothes he was wearing in my vision, was just as he was in a photo that Dad had of him!

On another occasion when Mum and I were in a very old building, and I had one hand on a very old door, I went into a trance and shouted '*I need to get to the banquet, I need to get to the banquet*'. Mum asked me what I meant, I repeated and repeated the words. She insisted there was no such event that she knew of, but she asked a member of staff about a banquet and he told us there had been an important one there at some time in history.

There had been other similar unexplained experiences around that time!

All this trauma put a strain on the family, including Mum and Dad's marriage, which ended in them parting and later going through a divorce. India and me still see Dad and spend nice times with him.
.
The following is a heartfelt article that Mum wrote in the Tuberous Sclerosis Scan magazine in August.

"Well 1996 has now passed and I must say that it has been another busy year, during which we have been involved with fund raising for the TSA. We started with another one of our successful discos which raised £1,000. Billy and I were pleased to hand over the cheque from the disco in November at the TSA AGM held in Birmingham. In addition, a great deal of time has been spent assisting with other fund raising events which had raised a grand total of £4,052.66 in the year so, once again, from the Norwich area comes a contribution to help towards the research of the condition.

Jack is now 4½ years old and has started part time school in September and this has been a great success. He is supported by a one to one helper for the time he is in school. Jack was statemented and hopefully he will remain in mainstream school. He is physically able and we are pleased to say that after spending so much of his short life in accident and emergency with very complicated fits, we have been fit free since February 1996, and have seen a great improvement in his learning and concentration skills. However Jack is still very tiring and life seems to be one great battle from the minute he wakes until he goes to bed.

It has become obvious that the older TS children get, the less acceptable their behaviour becomes to the general public and we still live life being subject of stares glares and comments that can, at times, be distressing. Most of us know that a trip to the local supermarket or shopping generally is a nightmare, but I continue to try these events every now and again hoping things may improve. Jack is now sleeping better and we don't spend so many sleepless nights by his side, suffering the torment that those who live with TS will recognise as being part of life. We are thankful for Jack's progress and very much aware that there are many who suffer more severely from the condition.

Jack was once again chosen for the Royal College of Physicians RCP (UK) Examinations at the Norfolk & Norwich Hospital. We were so pleased about this as Tuberous Sclerosis will remain clearly embedded in the minds of the doctors who examined Jack and diagnosed his condition during their training period. Jack was on form that day! His concentration level was low and hyper-activity high. I do not think the physicians will quickly forget him or the symptoms of his condition!

Jack was very lucky to have our local supermarket donate a computer CD Rom which he has mastered and in our opinion this has changed our lives. For the first time Jack will sit down and become involved in learning. Today there are so many educational CDs to choose from and we find he can learn so much from these, and he actually wants to. He amazes us by doing 9 year old tests on the computer, yet he still has trouble writing his name by hand. He has become very proficient at using the computer in a relatively short time and is becoming quite a computer whiz kid. He leaves us behind and I have now had to take computer night classes so that I can understand what is going on!

Well, we never thought we would see Jack go to mainstream school and be fit free for so long and this has been so encouraging for us. We can only hope this progress continues, and we are so thankful to the TSA for the support which they have given us since |Jack was diagnosed.

We recommend that all TS families should take advantage of the support and encouragement which the Association can offer. We hear such sad and heartbreaking stories from some of our members and I know that the worst is in the back of our minds from time to time. However we, as a family, want to dedicate some of our time to raise the awareness of Tuberous Sclerosis in the community generally and try to continue fund raising events in the hope that all TS sufferers and their families can benefit. Thanks to all friends, family and acquaintances who have supported us through 1996. "

Getting back to my own recollections, because of my poor co-ordination and some learning difficulties, I couldn't master the skill of riding a bike. This caused me a lot of frustration which, regrettably, I took out on Mum! In fact, I couldn't do simple tasks like tying my own shoelaces, and writing was still a massive challenge.

However, strangely enough, I learned to swim quite quickly. I have since learned that riding a bike can be a dangerous occupation and maybe its best that I missed out on that health hazard!

The art of multi-tasking has eluded me all my life. If asked to do an exercise in three parts, the best I can do is to complete just one of them. Parts 2 and 3 have to be repeated individually!

I've always loved all types of music and found I had a head for remembering songs by just hearing them once or twice. When I was seven I started learning to play keyboard. Every other Tuesday my teacher, Michael, came to give me lessons.

Unfortunately, Michael became ill and had to be taken into hospital, and our lessons came to an end. This was such a pity as Michael was well acquainted with kids with learning difficulties as he had a younger brother with similar problems. Therefore, he had the patience that was needed to help me through.

Mum decided to find another teacher for both me and India. She arranged for us to have lessons at a local music shop. However, the tutor was not prepared for two hyper-active kids such as us! He didn't have the patience and understanding that Michael had! We didn't progress at all with this person and lessons came to an abrupt end. At that stage I decided to try to teach myself, and although it was a long process, I was able to make some progress.

Around this time I liked to spend some spare time writing rap lyrics based on a TSC theme. A few are shown below, and then followed by a photo of me at the keyboard trying to teach myself!

Help! - I got Obstacles
I got events coming up
Some work rolling up
I live each day through experience I gain
I know I'll have obstacles in me path
But through an' through I'm a strong young blood
Here to help other TSC sufferers in me spare time
I'll speak on skype with me friends on line
Jack Royall

Glory Be - TSC

I was born with TSC
Promised God I'd mark me gene
I've been to clinics here and there
Glory Be
I climbed upon me cream lounge chair
And who did I encounter there
But me international TSC friends
Success Never Ends
We started speaking in this year
And we made really good friends
We might have other things to do
But we'll arrange to see it through
Glory Be
We have to be aware
That it could be another date
Another time another year
But all the same it's part of God's rhyme
Success Never Ends

Jack Royall

Soul Rap
Quick quick quick, going go go go go
I'll be back – though I may not show
And if you feel that heavy beat
It's gonna hit you hard and feel so neat
But what you need to see and find
Is what you are and feel inside
Make sure you tell your peers
So you don't get butterflies
so take these tips to heart
Then you'll feel mighty wise
So listen up girls and listen up guys
What I'm telling you will make you realise
You don't need coke
and you don't need alcohol
All you need is a loving free soul
So follow me and achieve your goal
And then you'll feel renewed and whole
Jack Royall

JACK

For Jack the seizures which come with his TSC have often been life threatening and resulted in ambulance dashes to hospital. As a baby he stopped breathing several times and suffered a cardiac arrest in reaction to anti-epilepsy medication.

In spite of uncontrolled epilepsy, Jack attended mainstream school until doctors on a project he was involved in spotted threatening growth in his brain tumours. Surgery left Jack with impaired memory and cognitive function and tragically six years later the tell-tale symptoms of nausea and paralysis indicated that tumours were growing back. Jack's Mum Ally says:

"After the surgery Jack felt different. He had to have extra support and eventually change schools but he still achieved some GCSE's."

Normal teenage life, going out independently and pursuing a career and friendships eluded Jack as he generally felt unwell and couldn't be left unattended because of his epilepsy.

With the milestone of adulthood came another dramatic turning point in Jack's life. At 18 he was accepted on a clinical trial for a drug that might shrink his troublesome tumours.

Months later Ally and Jack hardly needed the confirmation from scans that Jack's tumours have reduced considerably because he felt so much better almost immediately. He could think more clearly and his skin patches disappeared. Jack says:

"I felt as if I was reborn"

The transformation in Jack's health has given him back his independence. He can now catch the bus by himself to the hospital where he is on a course for people with learning difficulties to gain invaluable work experience and work-related skills.

Hopeful that he'll soon be taken on as a hospital porter when his course finishes, Jack says;

"I know what patients are feeling from my own experiences in hospital, so I believe I can do a really good job."

It seems that this may be Jack's destiny as he recalls telling the porters; 'I'll be one of you guys one day,' on one of the many occasions he was in hospital as a child.

Active fundraisers over the years, Jack's family attribute the return of his health and future prospects to the beneficial effects of the trial. Ally says:

"It's been miraculous. Jack might never have this opportunity without The TS Association."

A copy of page 14 from the TSA Annual Report 2010/2011

9

Progress and Set-Backs

During this period of my life I was taking part in various medical studies for children with my condition. For example, looking into behavioural and language problems, and genetics in TSC, all being carried out in Cambridge, either at Addenbrooke's or Douglas House.

Between appointments at the NNUH, Addenbrooke's, and Douglas House, I was developing quite well, but suddenly a serious deterioration set in. My concentration levels slumped, my IQ dropped dramatically, the frequency of my seizures returned and increased, my speech suffered, my vision was noticeably impaired. Mum was becoming increasingly anxious that something was going wrong.

Urgent tests and scans revealed that the SEGA in my brain had grown from the size of an orange pip to that of a chestnut. This had a serious affect as it was blocking the flow of fluid through my brain and hydrocephalus had occurred. This situation had become life-threatening.

So, at the age of eight, I was admitted to Addenbrooke's with a view to having surgery to remove the SEGA to relieve pressure in my brain. Instead, a decision was made by the neurologists to fit an Ommaya Reservoir to drain fluid away. Despite this my seizures continued, and increased.

Approximately one year later, although only eight years old, I was transferred over to an <u>adult</u> neurological team, again based at Addenbrooke's. Shortly after that I was re-admitted for a pioneering seven hour operation to remove the brain SEGA which was slowly ruining my ability to learn and retain information, and I was having more seizures. To make things even worse, it was threatening my eyesight.

My neurologist and his team, were amazing; they did the very best they could and the surgery was quite successful. Although they'd taken the majority of the SEGA, it wasn't possible for the whole thing to be removed without potentially serious permanent brain damage. The quality of my life had been improved many times over, but the surgery had left some issues.

The procedure was absolutely essential to save my life; the fact remained that I'd had my brain cut into, and I'd lost some of my intellect as a result; my concentration and memory had suffered badly.

My recovery was slow but noticeable at first. After a while I went back to mainstream school but even with a one-to-one helper progress seemed to go on hold!

The monitoring at Douglas House continued, and it became obvious to all concerned, that just about all aspects of my learning process had come to a standstill and had in fact gone into reverse.

Here's an extract taken from an account that Mum wrote in the Scan Magazine in October 2021, not long after my brain surgery in Addenbrooke's:

"Jack is alive, and his little sister, India, who is six, is healthy. Jack has such a great personality. He is so funny, everyone loves him. He's got a great sense of humour, lots of friends and is a very happy child. And he has never once complained.

I've never once said 'Why me? Why us?' There's no point in being bitter because that's not going to help Jack and there are plenty of people worse off. At least we've got Jack and that's what keeps us going. He's such a special person. I'm not going to say that I don't hurt or that I don't cry. Sometimes I hear people complaining about small things and I think 'Oh get a life'.

While we were in Addenbrooke's I had the best sleep I'd had for a long time because I knew there were people there to look after Jack. The night before the operation I felt a nervous wreck. Jack knew he was having an operation but he didn't know the full story.

It's been hard on India too. She visited him in hospital and found it tough seeing him so ill. She loves her brother dearly. Whenever she gets a wishbone she always wishes that Jack didn't have Tuberous Sclerosis. I tell her to wish for something for herself – I know she would love a horse - but she always wishes for Jack.

I would like to thanks everyone who has asked after Jack and who has helped us. For the future, I'm not thinking about it at the moment I'm just happy we've got through his latest op and he's still got his memory. He's still Jack. But I have always got the fear that he can develop another tumour at any time in any organ of his body. Thanks to TSA for being there during our darkest moments".

I added these few of lines at the end of Mum's piece:

"Please help the TSA support TS children everywhere. We want to make them better. We want to save them. Please, please help"

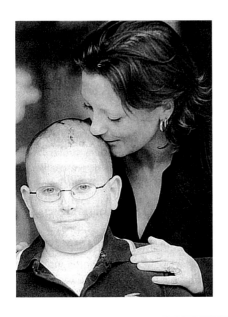
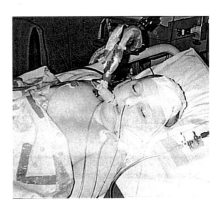
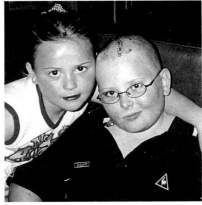

Black and white photos of me - one with Mum; one on my
own immediately after the op; and one with India; all taken
in Addenbrooke's.

10

More TSA Events

At the dawn of the new Millennium at a TSA Siblings Outing we were able to go on the London Eye and we were also invited to have tea at the houses of Parliament, an opportunity I would never have had if it hadn't been for TSC and the TSA!

During another TSA outing to the Apollo Theatre in Hammersmith I was one of 20 children chosen to stand up on stage and shake hands with the cast of Doctor Dolittle. This was exciting for an eight year old and his sister!

Thanks to the TSA we were able to go to a Taxi Fun Day in London when the Black Cab drivers were celebrating an important anniversary. On this visit we met a few celebrities and a bit later we went on a trip to the Millennium Dome, or as its now called, the 02 Arena.

In June of that year me and my family were invited to join a well-known singer and musician to a McDonalds in Great Yarmouth, close to where her family lived. We discovered we had lots in common; our birthdays are on the same day and our dads worked offshore. She told us how she had read the story in the local press about my brain surgery and she thought she would like to meet us.

Following that meeting we were invited as VIP guests to her concert at the old Wembley Arena. During the concert she invited my sister, India, to sing along side her on stage. Later that evening we went back stage. That was good fun, especially for India.

In December 2001 after lots of seizures the Tuberous Sclerosis Association invited us to a family day for sufferers and their parents to visit 10 Downing Street where we met the Prime Minister's wife and youngest child. So, you can see, although I had epilepsy and other health issues, my life wasn't all hospital appointments! Thanks to the TSA for these opportunities!

At one stage the local paper, the Eastern Evening News, ran a scheme called Local Heroes sponsored by a national gas company from which different people, including me, were nominated for what was called the Brave Child of the Year Award. Sadly, I wasn't the one chosen as the winner but that hadn't stopped me from taking part, and enjoying the event!

Moving on from there and when I was about nine Mum met Andy. He soon moved in to help Mum look after me and India. His support throughout the following years was great because, to be honest, the family really benefitted from him being with us as he took an active part in all aspects of our lives. Thanks Andy for being there and for becoming my friend as I've grown older.

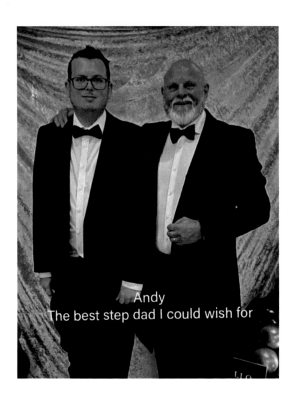

Andy
The best step dad I could wish for

11

Post-op Struggles

The time came when my school wanted me to start studying for nine GCSEs, I wasn't ready to cope with such a challenge. The school was not geared up to teach children of my age who weren't preparing for these tests. They followed the National Curriculum and didn't really know what to do with me as I didn't fall into any existing category.

As a result, I was put into the library every day, sometimes with just my one-to-one helper for company, and sometimes alone. This situation didn't do me much good!

After a while Mum decided that the school wasn't right for me and started to look at other possibilities.

Research led her to the Fred Nicholson School at Toftwood, about 18 miles from home. This is a school for pupils who have complex learning difficulties and they had a modified curriculum to suit the individual pupil.

I attended part of year 10 and year11 at Fred Nicks where I did Maths, English, Sex Education, Art and Woodwork. I became a library prefect. Whilst there, I performed keyboard in Assembly, which I enjoyed.

I still wasn't allowed to do P.E because of my epilepsy but I did embark on the Duke of Edinburgh Bronze Award Scheme. Unfortunately, I didn't get the Award because of the thing that had haunted me most of my life; Epilepsy!

The reason why epilepsy stopped me from getting the Duke of Edinburgh Award was because I wasn't allowed to stay over-night on camping trips, but they gave me a certificate for completing everything else.

In 2009, when I was 17, it was suggested that we could consider Vagal Nerve Stimulation in an attempt to reduce my seizures. This involves a stimulator being connected to the vagal nerve in the neck. It works by sending stimulation to areas of the brain by way of electrical impulses. After a lot of thought and research, Mum decided that it wasn't a treatment she wanted for me.

Just before Christmas 2007 I was taken very ill. One of the tumours had suddenly blocked the ventricle in my brain causing it to stop the flow of fluid, just as last time, before the surgery. Again, this resulted in hydrocephalus.

I was rushed to Addenbrooke's where I had an emergency procedure when a shunt was fitted to relieve the pressure in my brain caused by the build up of fluid. I was pleased to get home on Christmas Eve so that I could spend Christmas Day with my family. It was great to be able to open my presents at home!

When India, went back to school after that Christmas holiday the children in her class were asked by their teacher to write a story about something that had happened over Christmas. What follows is the very touching story that India wrote:-

"It was a week before Christmas when it triggered again like an ancient record that's stuck on repeat. I had a few friends over as school was out. Sitting on the floor in the living room, lights dimmed, watching Rocky Balboa. My nanny appeared, long faced, standing at the French doors. She took a deep breath. In that long waiting space my only thought was "why is she here?" I stood up sharply; she strolled into the opposite room, I followed.

I could hear my friends whispering and the TV still going, although my heart had come to a halt, I felt as though everything else should have. Nanny began to whisper; my heart started racing, everything gradually got louder, but not clearer. Then those words fell out of her dry mouth. "They have noticed there is something wrong with Jack he has had to stay in hospital for the night". I was searching for answers to all my questions, but there were too many. My Mum and brother were in Addenbrooke's Hospital, Cambridge, it seemed like they were a million miles away.

The next morning, after the news, I awoke at my friend Jade's house. I had refused to stay at my nanny's. But turning back to that page in my memory "SELFISH" was written all over me. I was supposed to be making things easier yet I was thinking of myself and trying to make life harder for everyone. But thinking now, all I really wanted was "attention" over the years when my brother Jack had been rushed into hospital for various reasons. I wouldn't say I felt neglected, but I felt a door would close on me, darkening, and I'd run and tuck myself in a corner hunched as if I were running from something (that's just how I felt). I just wanted someone to tell me that all would be OK.

Time was passing slowly. Jack had been in hospital for three day's by this time. My stepdad Andy drove me up to Cambridge to visit my Mum and Jack (I never liked being away from my Mum for long). From what I remember the journey had only a few words. I liked to peer out the car window watching the cars zoom past.

As soon we arrived I glared at the Hospital as if it were my worst enemy, but it was a lot bigger, more powerful and definitely stronger than me. We walked past the canteen in the hospital. The smell reminded me of school dinners, which I detest, and smelly old pensioners' homes. We marched to the ward that my brother had been referred to. Our footsteps echoed in my ears, gradually getting louder. The familiar smell of medication and plastic lingered.

Racing to see my brother, the mixed emotions are indescribable. I had to be strong, although my eyes felt like crashing waves. I felt angry, but I had to be happy

(I clenched my hands to hold in the pain and tears.) The hike felt never ending. Then I saw him there in that metal bed, tubes and needles poking from all directions of his body, I looked around the ward he was in, the sick children were to my left and right. I could feel my chin trembling; I then burst into tears. I thought to myself "I'm so grateful to be healthy". I bent down and gave Jack a hug; he held me tight, it felt like magic. He's a hero, strong and brave.

When they told me they didn't know whether Jack would be out for Christmas, I got a sudden lump in my throat. I never have believed in god, every time things happen like this I know for sure someone couldn't possibly be up there! Christmas Eve had come and I began to realise that Jack wouldn't be out for Christmas but at 11pm Christmas Eve they decided to let Jack come home. It was a miracle; my family and I had the best Christmas present ever Jack being home for Christmas."

What an amazing account of a 13 year old sibling's feelings!! It makes me feel so sad that India has had so many emotional episodes during her young life, and all through no fault of her own! And I wasn't thoughtful enough then to understand her feelings!

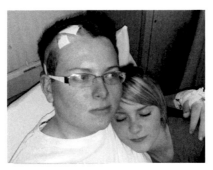

The top picture is of India and me when we were about five and seven, and the bottom one is of us together in Addenbrooke's

12

'You Alright Jack?'

When I was about 16 I wrote a piece for my Journal,
which I entitled 'You Alright Jack? I'm including this
next as it describes how, through my eyes, I saw the
attention other people (friends and family) gave me. I
was 16 then; I'm now 32 so I've double in age and so
much has happened in my life, and with my health, since
then. I no longer hear those three little words, but it
doesn't hurt to reflect back on that time when life was
different!

*'You Alright Jack?' These three little words are the
words most frequently spoken to me, or asked of me,
since I can first remember. They come from almost
everyone I know; my family; my friends and the many
carers that have been close to me for as long as long as I
can recall.*

*The words, at first glance, appear to be a question and,
frequently, they are. But often they're phrased in such a
way that they take on a very different meaning.
Sometimes they're uttered quietly, as if by habit, by*

someone who is seeking reassurance for themselves that, indeed, I am 'alright'.

I sometimes wonder if they're 'Alright' – they keep repeating themselves!

Other times they're spoken with concern, or with irritation if I don't respond with a 'yes' quickly enough. For example, when I'm in the bathroom and no noise has been heard from me for a few minutes. I'm not quite sure what sort of noise they expect to hear, bearing in mind where I am at the time!!

You may be wondering why there's such an interest in my being 'Alright'. Well I'll explain; I was born with a multi-faceted genetic disorder called Tuberous Sclerosis. Unfortunately, one of the symptoms of this condition is the formation of tubers in any organ of the body. I was born with four small ones in my brain, and this has resulted in me having several of the various forms of epilepsy.

I was first diagnosed with the disorder when I was about two and a half years old. There have been many changes in my medication over the years, and brain surgery.

You see, one type of epilepsy that I've experienced in the past means that I have to be resuscitated when I have a seizure. For this reason everyone around me ask those three little words 'You Alright Jack?' when I seem vague or quiet or any length of time.

So, I'll have to continue with the constant reassurance of those who care for me. After all, it doesn't take much effort to say 'YEAH' even though it may be many, many times a day.

My life has been a round of visiting many boffins with different specialities; professors, doctors, Mr this and Mr that; nurses neurologists, radiologists; psychologists, etc, etc. It's a brain-teaser trying to remember who specialises in what. Someone who is 'Alright' would never know these ologies and specialities exist!

Shortly after my diagnosis Mum learned of the Tuberous Sclerosis Association and we, as a family, became members. This was the best move Mum could have made as it gave her and the rest of the family, and friends, a chance to learn so much more about this little known condition, and to meet other families with the same problem. Mum tells me that the support from the Association kept her going when things were really bad.

Maybe one day. With the help of research and progress in the treatment of my condition, I'll be able to swap those three little words from:

'You Alright Jack?' to 'I'm Alright Jack!'

Much of what's in the account from my Journal has been repeated during this story, but including it here may help other sufferers and their families understand that the care and vigilance they are experiencing, the anxieties they feel, and the reassurances they seek are perfectly normal.

I understand that now, but I didn't then.

13

Various Learning Opportunities

And so the years ticked by; home, school, epilepsy, hospital; home, school, epilepsy, hospital; with a welcome outing here and there, arranged for the TSC community, by the TSA, to add some excitement to the routine that had become a way of life for me and my family. We did things with the TSA that we would never have done without them. Thanks again TSA!

After I'd finished my tailor-made GCSE's at Fred Nicholson School they recommended a two year course at Norwich City College which would suit my needs, it was called Phoenix Purple. This offered students with aspergers syndrome the opportunity to develop confidence, skills and experience to enable them to consider future employment. I enjoyed this and during that time I did cooking, English, IT at work, drama, and GCSE photography.

When I was 17 because Nanny knew how much I enjoyed music she asked me if I'd like to join a choir that she knew of; it was a group of about 12 members called 'Simply Friends' and they were just that, Friends! They made me very welcome and encouraged me and Nanny to join them on their weekly get-togethers at the leader, Alison's, house. I really enjoyed their company and they introduced me to the pleasure of singing in a group.

Nothing spectacular was expected of me; it was just an evening for a social get-together as well as rehearsing well-known songs, many from musicals. Occasionally, we all performed concerts at a local church that many of the Simply Friends members belonged to. On one such event I was encouraged to sing a solo, which I did and I enjoyed it. I made some really good friends there and although I'm no longer a regular member, I see them now and then, and I'm always welcome, just as before.

In October 2010 I was lucky enough to be placed at the NNUH on an educational scheme called Project Search. This is a programme which was originally set up in Cincinnati Children's Hospital USA to enable unemployed 18 to 25 year olds with various learning needs to go into the hospital for one academic year, with a mentor, to carry out work experience. The project was copied here in the UK.

Each individual had specific job roles allotted to them for the period of their time there. I worked in the health records department for one term, and as a porter for the other two terms. I felt secure in this work as I knew that if I had seizures I was in the right place for any care that may be needed.

I really enjoyed this experience as it involved more than just working; we had classroom sessions where we had tuition in many life skills, such as face to face communications, nutrition, health and safety, good hygiene, making and updating written and video CVs. I was one of the individuals chosen out of the group to present the coming year's proposals at open day.

Although there were one or two full-time jobs offered to students at the end of the course, I wasn't one of them. I was disappointed, but I'd had the experience and that was important!

Another opportunity came along; an interesting course was suggested to me – it was called Develop EBP which was a place for people with aspergers syndrome. I looked into it and went along for an interview and was accepted. I met a young lady who became my personal assistant on the course. Over the period September 2013 to June 2014 I learned about animation, graphic design, how to upgrade hardware on a computer, doing business online and finally making computer games.

After that I went back to City College in Norwich and did GCSE, Sociology English and Maths.

A bit later a relative of a TS friend, who lived in Norfolk and had a web-site building business, gave me the chance to go along to his nearby office to sit in on some of his work. This gave me a fantastic in-sight into the work done there and I was given the chance to learn the principles of web-building and coding. I really liked this work.

Unfortunately, COVID came along and the owner decided to transfer the operation to his home and work alone from there.

My next experience wasn't really a 'learning opportunity' in the true sense of the word, but it was a lovely experience and I learned a lot from it. Mum applied for me to be considered as a candidate for the 'Make a Wish' scheme. I was allocated a place and chose to go back to Florida – this is the place where I had my first fit and ended up in hospital. You may remember from earlier in this story I said that I wanted to go back there to see what I missed out on through being ill! This was my chance!

I was granted my wish and went to Orlando to swim with Dolphins. It was great and everything I could have wished for and there's a photo on the next page to prove that I really did it !!!!!

Me kissing a dolphin in Florida!

14

The EXIST3 Trial

With regard to my general health, things weren't going too well for me, in fact, it appeared to be deteriorating. Scans showed that what remained of the SEGA following surgery was growing. Small tumours in my eyes were growing; I'd developed tunnel vision. A tumour in one kidney had grown to the point that it was feared that it may rupture. A decision had to be made about possibly removing the kidney before it got worse.

This was just as I turned 18, and coincided with Mum learning about a trial of a new drug (RAD001) as a potential treatment for some TSC sufferers.

This was to be a five year trial (EXIST3) being conducted by Dr Chris Kingswood MBBS MSc FRCP (Consultant Nephrologist). It was decided that we should go for the trial instead of surgery to remove the kidney. We met Dr Kingswood at Saint George's University Hospital in Tooting, London, where he told us that he also had a clinic in the Royal Sussex County Hospital in Brighton.

My family agreed that if I were accepted on the trial, we would rather see Chris at the Brighton Clinic because, although it was a longer journey, we wouldn't have to worry about getting about London and the congestion charges that we would face there.

Andy drove us from Norwich to Brighton on each visit and we stayed in a hotel there because our appointments the next day were always at 9am. Thankfully, due to Andy's work, he was in a position to take us all the distance that was needed. In the early stages these visits were fortnightly appointments! I doubt that we would have been able to fulfil the requirements of the trial at such a distance, or in the Tooting clinic, without Andy's help and support.

The drug company refunded us with the costs of travelling and accommodation.

As part of the work involved with assessing my fitness prior to the trial I had to fast on the morning before arriving at the hospital so that they could take bloods and do other essential tests. Amongst other things I regularly had to use a lung function machine to measure lung capacity.

Due to the test on the lung function machine being a stipulation to qualify for the trial at the very start, I was the only participant who passed that part of the pre-assessment process.

For a couple of months or so I was the sole patient who had passed all the fitness levels for the trial until the drug company made an amendment; they removed the lung function requirement; this resulted in a few other patients being approved at that early stage of the trial. None of us knew whether we were being given the drug or a placebo!

It was a double-blind trial so neither the researchers nor the doctors working with us knew which of the participants were on the real drug and which were on a placebo.

However, my family believed that I was on the real drug right from the start because as a result of regular screening, it was obvious that my kidney, liver, eyes and brain tubers had shrunk quite noticeably, and the rash (facial angiomiolapomas) covering my face (a common symptom of TSC) was clearing up. Also, the subcutaneous nodules growing around my figure and toe nails (another common symptom) were disappearing. Surgery on my kidney was further delayed as a result of the reducing size of the tumour in there.

And so time passed and it was confirmed that I had been on the drug since the start of the trial. And so, I continued on as we were all confident that I was responding well as a result.

Because the drug has an immune suppressant affect, I was suffering a few side-effects, such as ulcers in my mouth, cellulitis, boils, MRSA and shingles, but these quickly cleared up with treatment and when the dosage of the drug was modified.

Between eight until 18 years my learning abilities had been on hold. I had become grossly overweight because some of the medications that I'd been on for years had made me sluggish and I was inactive. My short and long-term memory got worse. Since taking the drug I've had a lot of catching up to do! All was going well! I was becoming more active which resulted in me losing weight and becoming fitter.

The drug has helped bring back my long-term memory. I've found that going back to places has helped. For example, as I was driven around Norfolk, and further afield, things that had been tucked away at the back of my brain, for years, started to come back to me, such as people, places, songs and events.

I became capable of being left alone at home without risks of harming myself or burning the house down, or flooding it. I started going to the gym, and going out with friends and family members. I continued talking to other members of the TSC community in this country and around the world on Skype. Within the first year of being on the trial I went out alone and caught buses independently.

My seizures were under control for the first time in my life, and my autistic tendencies reduced. I no longer considered myself as being a person living with a disability, but a person living with controlled TSC and all that goes with it. In short, I became a different person!

Surprisingly, I coped really well with the changes taking place, and so quickly after starting the drug, Everolimus.

I can't thank Dr Chris Kingswood enough for entering me on this trial and seeing me through, this far. Its been an amazing journey, which has proven that however bad things are science and research bring the possibility of *light at the end of the tunnel.*

And we should not give up hope!

This is a photo of Mum and me. I'm holding a pack of
Everolimus – the drug that has changed my life

15

Public Speaking

My progress on the trial was so good that I was invited to speak at conferences concerning the drug and the way in which it was changing my life. I was asked to speak in Belfast, Sorrento, Birmingham, Henley, and Frimley, Surrey (then the Novartis Headquarters).

In Belfast I spoke to an audience of medical professionals. I had the pleasure of meeting and speaking to Dr Franz of Cincinnati Children's Hospital and other doctors from around the world, including a TSC doctor from Israel.

During my talk in Sorrento (in 2013) I had an audience of trainee doctors and Novartis staff. The main purpose of my visit and talk was to illustrate to those present just what an effect Everolimus had had on me. After my speech I was filmed for Novartis' website so that those actually working in the lab on the development of the drug could see for themselves the result of their labours.

Subsequently, an animated comic strip was made, entitled 'Turbo & Scott', being a collaboration between

Novartis and DC Comics. The strip can be viewed via the free graphic novel download on the Tuberous Sclerosis Association Website for Turbo & Scott.

In November 2011 I went with Mum to that year's TSA AGM where I delivered my speech to a combination of TSC patients and their families, and several health professionals, all with an interest in TSC, its symptoms and treatments. I explained how remarkable the change had been from the person I was, and the person I had become, as a result of the drug.

I explained that before the drug the purpose of my life was to be a patient, after which, the purpose of my life was to be a person!

Later that evening, several people spoke to me and said how uplifting the account of my life had been and the hope that my speech had given them.

There were families there who had known me (through the TSA) for many years, even since I was very young, and they were amazed at the change in me, as a result of being on the drug. One such lady who had known me since I was in first school, broke down and cried when she spoke to me; she couldn't believe that I was the same person!

At the top its me in Sorrento, and below is a picture of me with my Auntie Louise (that's one of Mum's sisters) who accompanied me to Sorrento

16

Funding

From the beginning of the trial, my involvement was funded by the company that developed the drug, Everolimus, that's Novartis Pharmaceuticals.

However, as the trial was coming to an end we became aware that the NHS was not prepared to fund use of the drug. This was worrying as I'd been told by the medical people monitoring my progress that if I stopped using Everolimus (due to cost or otherwise) the tumours that had so successfully reduced in size by up to 90% would re-grow!

I felt worried for myself and for the many other TSC sufferers who could be deprived of the benefits the drug had bought me, and this made me very sad.

There followed a campaign, instigated by Dr Chris Kingswood, to lobby Parliament to get the NHS to approve the drug for use by TSC patients. I decided to do whatever I could to get the NHS to approve the drug and to fund it so I wrote to our local MP here in Norwich asking her to help our campaign. I'm now including a few paragraphs from my letter dated 24th April 2014:

'I was fortunate in being the first person in the UK to be accepted on the trial for this drug. I was very lucky to be part of Dr Kingswood's research program which was paid for by Novartis Pharmaceuticals, the company that developed RAD001 (Everolimus).

Since starting on the trial, and being aware of its benefits, I've spoken at conferences, one of which was in Belfast where I spoke in front of 150 doctors and geneticists, and another was in Sorrento where I was filmed for Novartis' website, so the scientists who developed the drug in the laboratories could be made aware of my progress.

On behalf of myself, and thousands of other TSC sufferers (and those still unborn) and their families, I shall be grateful if you will do all that you can to press our Government to support the needs of those who are suffering the devastating effects of rare diseases, including TSC, and to fund new drugs and their use, as they become available.'

I was delighted to learn that in 2019 that the NHS had approved Everolimus and would fund its use for TSA patients with epilepsy that isn't controlled by other medication. This is a massive step forward for the TSC community.

Me in blue – and that's Mum in white!

17

And Now

I'm now 32 and apart from a few autistic/aspergers tendencies. I'm doing Ok. What issues I have are reasonably well managed with medication and plenty of support! Happily I haven't had a seizure for a long time.

In 2014 I was allocated a Housing Association bungalow, which is on a small development reserved for adults or families with complex health or social needs. It's about a mile from where Mum lives, so that's great as she gives me a lot of help.

Yes, I need help to manage my life and over the years I've had a number of very special personal assistants/support workers to provide the help I need other than the things that Mum does for me.

I like spending time with India and her twin boys (my nephews) Ocean and Orlando; now three years old!

One photo is of the twins with India, and the other is of the twins without India but with ice creams instead!

I have a few hobbies that I enjoy, like collecting Assassins Creed comics and paraphernalia; I enjoy the cinema and sometimes go with Andy and other mates, and I go to the gym sometimes where Dad is a sports coach. Thanks Dad for all your help and support; you are my Dad and my friend.

I do a lot of gaming on-line with my best mate, Mitch, and one or two other mates. Mitch lives several miles away from me but we meet up in person, now and again, as well as on-line.

I've done a lot of on-line studying in subjects connected with IT in one way or another, and I'm now looking into other courses.

I've had one or two girl-friends over the years but at the moment I'm a happy singleton.

I like communicating on-line with a few TSC friends in different places around the world, and I have a good TSC mate called Laurence who lives in Newcastle who I met at a TSA function a few years ago, and we keep in touch.

I've recently been to visit him and his family and stayed for a weekend in his house. My Dad drove us there and then he went off to see an old mate who he hasn't seen for years. While I was there I went with Laurence and his family to a Pyromusical Fireworks Spectacular at Bishop Auckland –which was AMAZING!

Pictures of me and Mitch (top) and with Laurence below

18

And Thanks

I'll close my story by thinking about just some of the people and organisations that have been there for me and my family along the journey.

Some of those that I want to mention are the many medical professionals, from my GP surgery to those at the various hospitals and clinics that have helped me over the years.

I'd like to say thank you to all the personal assistants/support workers, who from time to time, have been there for me; they've been great and we've had some fun times.

Then there's our Heartsease Friends, especially Kerrie and Lorraine and their families… thanks guys.

But most of all I want to thank my family here in Norfolk and in Cheshire, and that includes my aunties and uncles, and all of my cousins, for their endless encouragement, love and support, not just for me but for Mum and India as well. I can't imagine our lives without them!

And special thanks to Nanny Pam and her sister Auntie Trish who have travelled every step of the way with us.

Here I am with my Aunties Lesley (left)
And Louise (right) (Mum's sisters)

84

Left Auntie Trish; right Nanny Pam;
and I'm the one in the middle!

I know I'm so lucky to be as well as I am when there are many others who are suffering some of the more severe complications that TSC can throw at us, and our families, as a consequence.

What follows is an encouraging report by Pooja Takhar that summarise the amazing progress being made in research and development in medical science that will help the TSC community, from diagnosis and onwards.

Hopefully, this will result in many of us living longer, better and more fulfilling lives. Thank you Pooja for bringing us up-to-date in this way:

An Up-to-date Summary of Medical Research and Scientific Developments in the Treatment of TSC - May 2024

Report by Dr Pooja Takhar - Joint Chief Executive – TSA

This is a very exciting time for TSC research as remarkable progress in both clinical and translational research has resulted in several new treatments for tuberous sclerosis complex or TSC. With Everolimus and Epidyolex now approved and available to the TSC community on the NHS, there is a growing list of medicines that may become available for people with TSC in the near future.

Starting with those that are most advanced in the clinical trial cycle is the topical sirolimus cream **Hyftor** which is developed by Nobel Pharma for TSC-associated facial angiofibromas (a disfiguring rash). In 2003, the Medicines and health Regulatory Agency of the UK (MHRA) confirmed that Hyftor is safe and effective for TSC-associated facial angiofibromas so the decision makers in the UK nations are now considering whether to fund the treatment on the NHS.

Another clinical trial which is already underway in US and several other countries and expected to start in the UK soon, is the **TrustTSC** trial. It is a global Phase 3 study by Marinus Pharma exploring whether treatment with their drug, called ganaxolone, can reduce the frequency of seizures associated with TSC in children and adults.

The TSA is very proud of the role it is playing in a new trial with the drug Epidyolex or cannabidiol. **Epidyolex** was approved for refractory epilepsy in 2023, the company is now interested to study whether it also improves behavioural outcomes in people with TSC.

TSA has been involved in the clinical trial right from the beginning with several community members given the opportunity to comment on the design and methodology of the clinical trial. MHRA has approved the drug for new clinical trial.

Another pharmaceutical company called Noema Pharma is developing **basimglurant,** a drug with a new mechanism of action and a potential treatment of seizures associated with TSC. There are 6 clinical trial sites in the UK who are currently recruiting children older than 5 years, adolescents and adults up to 30 years of age to participate in the study.

Longboard, a US-based pharmaceutical company, is developing and testing a compound called LP352 as a potential treatment of seizures associated with Dravet syndrome, Lennox-Gastaut syndrome (LGS) TSC, CDKL5 deficiency disorder (CDD) and other epileptic disorders. It's called **Pacific study**. It's in early stages and conducting clinical trial in the US.

Aeovian is a US-based biopharmaceatical company developing novel and highly selective treatment for TSC-associated seizures.

UCB Pharma have recently applied to National Institute for Clinical Excellence (NICE) to get funding on the NHS for their drug fenfluramine for LGS. The company is next planning to extend the clinical trial to include TSC so potentially another treatment for TSC.

The TSA is proud of our role and impact in the huge progress we've seen in TSC research and treatments. In addition to funding and influencing TSC research we will continue to advocate for access to new, innovative medicines that people with TSC deserve.

Not every TSC sufferer will find their *magic bullet* in a Pill called Everolimus, a life-changing drug developed and produced by Novartis Pharmaceuticals. But as can be seen from Pooja's summary, with ongoing research and development, hopefully, there will be benefit for other categories of patients for which meaningful help is yet to be found.

I really hope that will be the case.

And I hope that sharing my experience with you all will give hope and encouragement to other TSC sufferers and their families.

Jack Royall

A recent picture of me